HÄGAR

THE HORRIBLE

HÄGAR IN TROUBLE

by Dik BROWNE

ATTICA
PUBLICATIONS

England.

© 1986 King Features Syndicate Inc.
Yaffa Character Licensing London.

First published by Attica Publications 1986

An imprint of Argus Communications Ltd.,
DLM House, Edinburgh Way, Harlow,
Essex CM20 2HL, England.

ISBN 1 85176 055 5

Printed in Holland

HÄGAR The Horrible

by DIK BROWNE

NOW, IF NOBODY STOPS ME, MAYBE I CAN STILL SEE THE FELLOWS TONIGHT...

JUST A MINUTE, DADDY

DRAT!

DADDY, SIT DOWN. LUTE IS GOING TO PLAY A SONG FOR YOU!

AW, DO I GOTTA?

OKAY, BUT MAKE IT FAST

HE JUST HAS TO TUNE UP FIRST

PLINK PLINK

PLINK
PLINK
PLINK
PLINK!
MY DOG HAS FLEAS...

PLINK

MY DOG HAS FLEAS...

PLINK PLINK PLINK

AW! PLAY THE ◎☆✕!!! THING!!

SPRANG!!

OH, NOW HE HAS TO TUNE IT ALL OVER AGAIN!

BOING!

DIK BROWNE 4-24

HÄGAR The Horrible — by DiK BROWNE

HÄGAR The Horrible
by Dik Browne

YOU GOT A NICE TOWN, HAGAR

WE LIKE IT

BUT DON'T YOU WORRY ABOUT INVADERS?

NAW! VIKINGS DON'T WORRY

AREN'T YOU AFRAID THE HUNS WILL ATTACK YOUR VILLAGE?

NOT WITH OUR EARLY WARNING SYSTEM

AT THE FIRST SIGN OF DANGER ALL LUCKY EDDIE HAS TO DO IS PULL THAT CHAIN

IT DROPS 10 BIG LEAD BALLS ON A BIG BASS DRUM WITH A NOISE LOUD ENOUGH TO WAKE UP THE WHOLE TOWN!

BAM BOOM BAM BOOM

BUT TO MAKE SURE — IT WAKES UP 12 SQUEAKING GEESE AND KNOCKS OVER 20 EMPTY DUSTBINS!

HONK BAM CLANK EEEK KWAAK BAM

WOW! THAT'S A NOISE!

YOU BET! NO ENEMY IS GOING TO SURPRISE US WITH OUR WARNING SYSTEM

1-2

IT'S FOOL-PROOF

Z

HÄGAR The Horrible

by DIK BROWNE

YOU KNOW, THE ENGLISH REALLY KNOW HOW TO PUT ON A SHOW

AND THEY DO IT WITH SUCH CLASS! LOOK AT THIS!

WOW

THE ENGLISH SURE LOVE CEREMONIES

LOOK! HERE COMES THE ROYAL HERALD

HE MUST BE GOING TO MAKE AN ANNOUNCEMENT!

BY ROYAL DECREE, REFUSE WILL BE COLLECTED ONLY ON TUESDAYS AND FRIDAYS

DIK BROWNE
11-14

HÄGAR The Horrible

by DIK BROWNE

REMEMBER — I DON'T WANT TO CATCH YOU DRINKING OR FIGHTING TONIGHT!

ME, NEITHER!

I'M SICK OF YOU CAUSING A RIOT EVERY TIME WE GO OUT!

AW...

I WANT YOU TO BEHAVE YOURSELF AT THIS PARTY! DO YOU HEAR?

I HEAR, I HEAR

STAY OUT OF TROUBLE AND TRY TO STAY NEAT!

YEAH, NEAT...

WAIT A MINUTE... LET ME FIX YOUR SHOELACE —

HEY! NOT SO TIGHT — YOU DON'T WANT TO STOP MY CIRCULATION!

THAT'S THE IDEA

4-17

DIK BROWNE

HÄGAR The Horrible

by Dik BROWNE

TODAY I GO TO MAKE MY FAME, TO ADD "EXPLORER" TO MY NAME

DESTINY CALLS AND I MUST GO TO SEARCH THE WORLD BOTH HIGH AND LOW

♪ HÄGAR ♪

I GO TO FIND THE MYSTIC GRAIL, THE GOLDEN FLEECE, THE GREAT WHITE WHALE

AND LOST ATLANTIS I'LL RECOVER AND KING TUT'S TREASURE I'LL DISCOVER

THE FOUNTAIN OF YOUTH, I'LL FIND THAT SPOT, THE ELEPHANTS' GRAVEYARD, I ALMOST FORGOT!

JUMBO

THE MALTESE FALCON AND, OH, YES, I'LL FIND THE MONSTER OF LOCH NESS

LOST WORLDS, LOST CHORDS AND I THINK IF I HAVE TIME ... THE MISSING LINK

AND STILL MORE THINGS I'M GOING TO DO .... AS SOON AS I FIND MY OTHER SHOE

?

HÄGAR The Horrible

by DIK BROWNE

THE TIDE IS UP... THE SHIP IS READY— WHAT DO WE DO?

ONE MINUTE

I GOT MY MAPS AND MY LUCKY RABBIT FOOT.... ONE MORE THING AND WE'LL BE READY TO TAKE OFF

DO WE INVADE ENGLAND?

IT DEPENDS ON THE WEATHER

LUCKY EDDIE IS CHECKING THE COWS NOW

COWS?

SURE, DON'T YOU KNOW? WHEN COWS STAND UP, IT MEANS FAIR WEATHER —

BUT WHEN THEY LIE DOWN, IT MEANS BAD WEATHER

AH! HERE'S LUCKY EDDIE NOW!

WHAT'S THE WEATHER FORECAST?

DON'T ASK!

DIK BROWNE 9-10

HÄGAR The Horrible

by Dik BROWNE

HÄGAR The Horrible
by DIK BROWNE

WELCOME TO THE FIRST ANNUAL PEACE AND FRIENDSHIP BALL

JUST PARK YOUR AXES IN THE HALL

AND LET THE DANCE BEGIN!

WOULD YOU JOIN ME IN A LITTLE GENTEEL DANCE?

DELIGHTED

YOU KNOW, FOR A BIG MAN, HAGAR IS VERY LIGHT ON HIS FEET!

LA-DE-DA!

OW! MY FOOT!

OAF!

I'M SORRY

HEY! WHO ARE YOU SHOVING?!

TAKE THAT!!

YOU CAN'T DO THAT

OW!

2-6
DIK BROWNE

HEY, LOOK, SVEN! I THINK TOUCH DANCING *IS* COMING BACK!

HÄGAR The Horrible

by DIK BROWNE

I DON'T CARE HOW MANY PEOPLE BELIEVE IT— I THINK IT'S A MYTH

AND YET ...THEY SAY THAT BEHIND EVERY MYTH THERE'S A GRAIN OF TRUTH... I WISH I KNEW.

I WISH GROWN-UPS WOULDN'T MAKE SUCH A MYSTERY ABOUT EVERYTHING

ALL THAT KIDS ARE ASKING FOR ARE A FEW SHORT, HONEST ANSWERS INSTEAD OF A LOT OF DOUBLE TALK...

DAD, CAN I ASK YOU A QUESTION?

OF COURSE

WOULD YOU TELL ME WHERE BABIES COME FROM?

NO

WELL, IT **WAS** SHORT AND HONEST!

3-20

DIK BROWNE

HÄGAR The Horrible

by DiK BROWNE

HÄGAR The Horrible
by DIK BROWNE

5-16   DIK BROWNE

HÄGAR The Horrible

by Dik BROWNE

IS THAT A ROCK I SEE?

IT COULD BE A SMALL WHALE OR A BIG SEAL OR A SPOT OF SEAWEED....

IT'S A ROCK!

CRASH!

HAGAR! THE SHIP IS SINKING!

DON'T WORRY—I'LL GET SOME HELP

WE'RE LOST! THERE ISN'T A BOAT TO HELP US WITHIN A HUNDRED MILES!

AW, DON'T PANIC

HERE — RUN THIS FLAG UP THE MAST

?

IT NEVER FAILS

DIK BROWNE - 2-27

HÄGAR The Horrible
by DIK BROWNE

HÄGAR The Horrible
by DIK BROWNE

SEE THIS? THIS IS MY HOROSCOPE

I ONLY WISH I HAD THIS YEARS AGO — MY LIFE WOULD HAVE BEEN DIFFERENT...

MY BIGGEST MISTAKE WAS MARRYING A *LEO!*

LEO'S ARE BOSSY, LOUD, DUMB AND DON'T COME HOME WHEN THEY'RE SUPPOSED TO! *VIRGOS* ARE JUST THE OPPOSITE!

VIRGOS ARE NEAT, HARDWORKING, GOOD-LOOKING AND INTELLIGENT

AND THE STARS DON'T LIE!

BRAVO!! THAT'S BRILLIANT!

SEE?! EVEN LUCKY EDDIE UNDERSTANDS THAT!

OF COURSE— I'M A VIRGO MYSELF!

2-20

⇒SIGH⇐

RIP!

HERE, OL' FRIEND HAVE A DRINK!

DIK BROWNE

HÄGAR The Horrible
by Dik BROWNE

HÄGAR The Horrible
by DiK BROWNE

HÄGAR The Horrible
by DIK BROWNE

HÄGAR The Horrible

by DIK BROWNE

HÄGAR The Horrible

by DIK BROWNE

HELGA, MY STOMACH TELLS ME IT'S...

YOUR STOMACH! ALL YOU THIN ABOUT IS YOL STOMACH

IT'S WORSE THAN HAVING A WOMAN FOR A RIVAL!

AW, YOU CAN'T BE JEALOUS OF MY POOR LITTLE STOMACH...

LISTEN! I'M SICK OF YOUR STOMACH COMING BETWEEN US! EITHER LOSE THAT POT OR I'M LEAVING!

LOSE MY STOMACH? AFTER ALL WE'VE BEEN THROUGH TOGETHER?

THE CUSTARD PIE SHORTAGE OF '63 ...THE CHOCOLATE CHIP PANIC... SNACKLESS DAYS ...REMEMBER HOW I NURSED YOU THROUGH THE COLIC?

AND THEN THERE WERE THE GOOD TIMES... OUR FIRST STEWED OX PIE... TRIPLE-DIP SUNDAES...THE DAY WE DISCOVERED SECONDS...

DIK BROWNE 10-17

AND YOU'VE GROWN AND MATURED AND BECOME LIKE A PART OF ME...

AND NOW SHE SAYS I MUST CHOOSE BETWEEN YOU AND HER...

I'D BETTER START TO PACK.

HÄGAR The Horrible

by Dik BROWNE

HÄGAR The Horrible

by DIK BROWNE

WHAT A STRANGE AND SQUIRMY DAY

THE SUN IS BRIGHT BUT FEELS LIKE ICE

IT COULD ONLY MEAN ONE THING....

IT IS *THAT* TIME AGAIN...

NOW IS THE TIME...THE LAST LEAF FALLS ...THE NIGHTS GROW LONG ...THE DAYS GROW COLD...

NOW PUT AWAY ALL RICH FOODS AND WINES AND SUCH...

BANISH FROM SIGHT ALL OPULENCE AND LUXURY...

DIK BROWNE

AND PUT ON RAGS AND TAKE UP THE BEGGAR'S BOWL...

AND WAIT, AS WAIT YOU MUST UNTIL...

TAP
TAP

THE TAX MAN COMETH

ENTER, FRIEND. WE HAVE NOTHING TO HIDE...

1-30

HÄGAR The Horrible

by DIK BROWNE

HEY! IT MUST BE TIME TO EAT

WHAT DO YOU WANT TO EAT?

I DON'T KNOW... THERE ARE SO MANY DIFFERENT PLACES TO EAT OUT IN THIS CITY...

FRENCH RESTAURANTS MAKE ME FEEL DUMB — I NEVER KNOW WHAT I'M ORDERING...

Chez COOCOO

FOOD'S NICE

FORGET IT

LET'S TRY THIS ENGLISH PLACE. AT LEAST I CAN UNDERSTAND WHAT I'M GETTING!

EVENING, GENTS — WHAT'LL YOU HAVE?

WHAT HAVE YOU GOT?

INKEY–DINKEY... BUBBLE AND SQUEAK... COCK-A-LEEKIE... BANGERS AND BLOATERS... ...TREACLES AND TRIFLES — ROLY POLY OR FIGGIE HOBBIN

WHAT DO YOU SAY?

I THINK THERE'S A CHINESE JOINT DOWN THIS WAY — LET'S TRY IT

5-1 DIK BROWNE

HÄGAR The Horrible
by DIK BROWNE

HÄGAR The Horrible

by DIK BROWNE

Look out for these forthcoming new exciting Hagar products in your local giftshops and bookshops.

- **●Cartoon Books●More Albums●**
- **●Wall Calendars●**
- **●Reminder Calendars●Diaries●**
- **●Greeting Cards for all Occasions●**
- **●Postcards●Posters●Stick-Em-Ups●**
- **●Gift Wrap●Gift Tags●**

For more details contact:
**Argus Communications Ltd.,
DLM House, Edinburgh Way, Harlow, Essex, CM20 2HL.
Tel: (0279) 39441.**